Holly Celebrates
Passover

Written by Kimberly Kendall-Drucker

Holly Celebrates Passover

Library of Congress Control Number: 2022904241

Hardback ISBN: 979-8-9859369-0-2

Paperback ISBN: 979-8-9859369-1-9

For the Drucker Family
Particularly my mothers-in-law **Marla** and **Ronnie**
who shared their recipes, traditions, and love -
my father-in-law, **Herb** whose contagious laughter and joy
lit up every Seder and every room,
and as always - *my Beloved* **Larry.**

There are special dates throughout the year
We call them holidays.
People love to celebrate them
In a gazillion different ways.

When you're born with a name like Holly
Well, you celebrate them ALL -
The **HOLLY-Days** of Summer, **Winter**
And of Springtime *and* of Fall.

When Winter turns to Spring
And birds come back to sing their song
My favorite Holly-Day
Will soon be here before too long.

It's a day on the Hebrew Calendar.
So, its date changes year-to-year.
But once Spring has the first full moon
Passover will be here.

Passover celebrates The *Exodus*
When the Israelites were freed
From being slaves in Pharaoh's kingdom
Escaping bondage, wrath, and greed.

Pharaoh did not want to free them.
He held on with all his might.
God sent *10 Plagues* to convince him
And help Pharaoh see the light.

God sent blood and boils and pestilence
And frogs and locusts too.
He sent beasts and bugs and hail
That shook the Pharaoh through and through.

Then He sent a chilling darkness.
Not one soul could see one sight.
But the last and deadly plague God sent
Passed Over the Israelites.

That's how **Passover** got its name.
Each year the story's told
At Seders all around the world
And it never gets old.

A Seder is a special dinner
Filled with family, food, and love.
We read the story of our freedom.
We give thanks to God above.

We'll all read from a Haggadah
That's the book that tells the story
Of when the Jews were slaves in Egypt
And our lives were filled with worry.

Everyone will take a turn to read
As soon as we get started.
We'll read how Moses led the Israelites
And how the Red Sea parted.

In the Haggadah you can also find
The best Passover songs.
Daddy sings loudly and festively
As we all sing along.

We sing a song to tell Old Pharaoh
Pharaoh, Let My People Go.
You cannot sing it in a normal voice.
You make your voice sound deep and low.

We use special plates and dishes
That we don't use for everyday.
This is my Bubbe's wedding china
And Mommy keeps it tucked away.

In the center of the table
Sits a very special platter
And it holds all the symbols
Of this holiday - that really matter.

Bubbe Ronnie liked to put an orange
Atop that Seder Plate.
To show that women can do anything,
And I think that's just great.

Mommy makes so much delicious food.
I try to help her cook.
We use my Bubbe Marla's recipes
She left us in her cookbook.

Our family comes to share from near and far
I think that's just the best.
We set places and move furniture
To make room for all our guests.

It's a welcoming and festive meal.
Let all who are hungry eat.
Still, it's not a day for mac and cheese
Or flour, bread, or wheat.

We eat unleavened bread called Matzoh -
A flat cracker without yeast.
While it might taste a little different
It's yummy with the Seder feast.

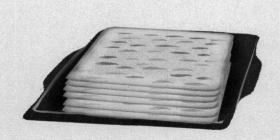  

Daddy loves the fluffy matzoh balls
He eats gefilte fish.
And he double-dips his parsley
In a salted-water dish.

My favorite is yummy charoset.
Aunt Kay and Daddy always make it.
It's packed with apples, nuts, and honey.
I can hardly wait to taste it.

Sometime before the dinner ends,
The middle matzah's broken,
When the dinner is all over
The kids search for the Afikomen.

The lucky kid who finds it
Always wins a special treat.
We scatter to find it quickly
Because there is still dessert to eat.

When the grownups finish having coffee
And the kids start getting sleepy
This year's Seder's at an end -
And we all feel a little weepy.

We shout *Next Year in Jerusalem*
As we all say good night
It means we cherish peace and freedom.
We want to live in love and light.

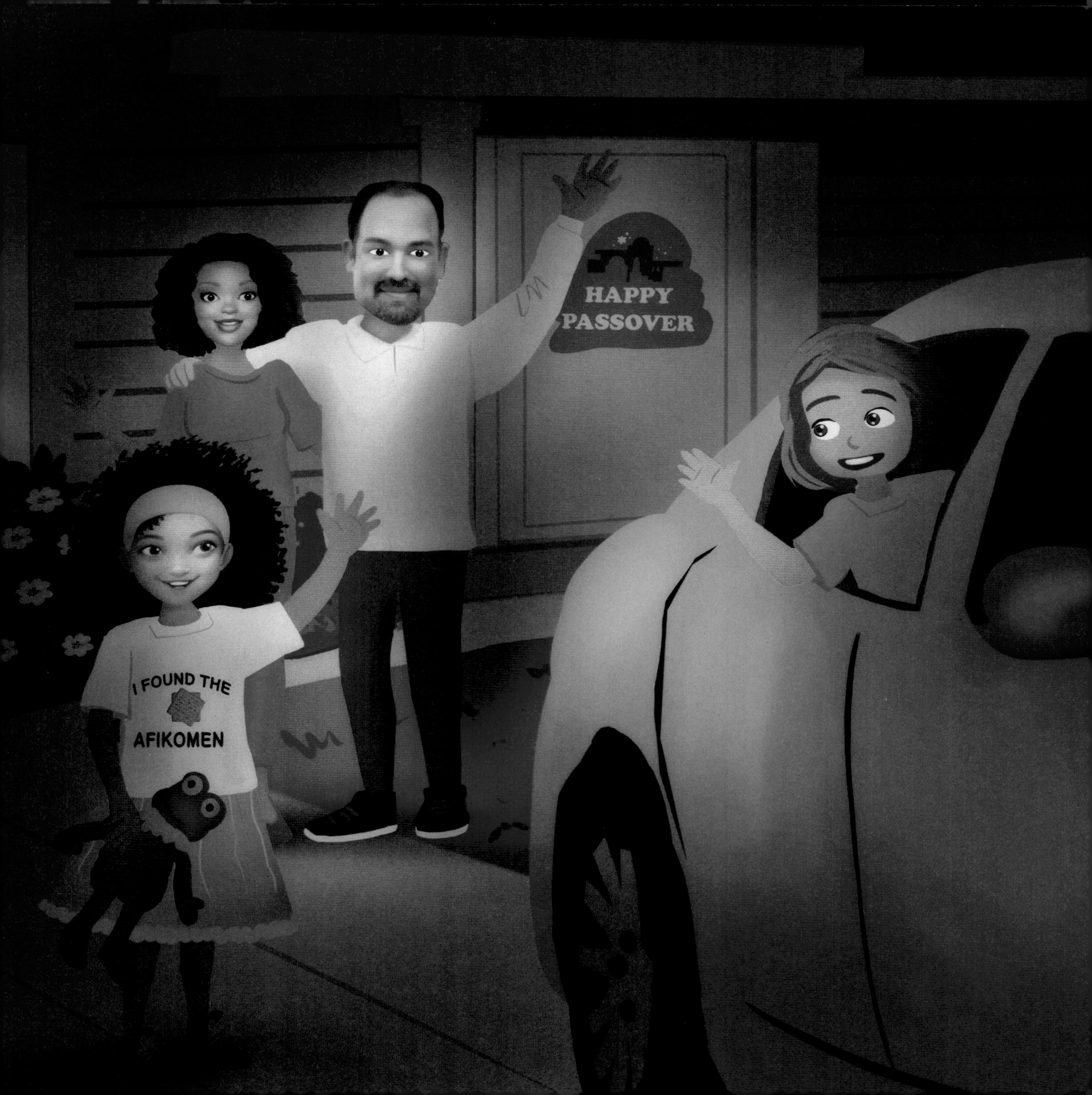
HAPPY
PASSOVER
I FOUND THE
AFIKOMEN

The Seder's not just about the past.
It's about the present too
And all the ways we *pursue justice*
In everything we say and do.

Maybe next year you can join us
We'll set a place and move a seat
We will welcome and make room for you
Let all who are hungry, come and eat.

Happy Passover from our house to yours!
Next Year in Jerusalem!

The End

Next in the Series:
Holly Celebrates Juneteenth
Holly Celebrates Independence Day
Holly Celebrates Summer Vacation

About the Author

Kimberly Kendall-Drucker lives in Charlotte, North Carolina with her husband Larry and Persian kitty, Zuzu. She loves reading, and her books are her friends. Her favorite childhood books are *Where the Sidewalk Ends, Roll of Thunder Hear My Cry, A Wrinkle in Time,* and *Are You There, God? It's Me Margaret.* Kimberly reads a book a week – sometimes two. She is committed to writing accessible books children enjoy - because readers are leaders.

Kimberly loves *Phase 10*, macaroni and cheese, the Oxford Comma, and graphic tees. She is currently obsessed with *Wordle.* Jeopardy is her favorite TV show. While some people are outdoorsy, Kimberly is decidedly indoorsy. Still, she loves a day at the beach. For Kimberly, *family is everything,* and her nieces and nephews are her pride and joy.

Holly Celebrates Passover is the fourth book in the *Holly Celebrates Series* and is Kimberly's fifth children's book.

To contact Kimberly or learn more about her, check out her website – **kimberlykendalldrucker.com**.

Made in United States
Orlando, FL
14 April 2022

16806747R00020